BREAKFAST SHOW BOOK

IN AID OF HELP A LONDON CHILD

CHRIS TARRANT'S

BREAKFAST SHOW BOOK

95·8 CAPITAL FM

® BANTAM BOOKS

LONDON · NEW YORK · TORONTO · SYDNEY · AUCKLAND

CHRIS TARRANT'S BREAKFAST SHOW BOOK

All royalties donated to Help a London Child

A BANTAM BOOK : 0 553 50550 5

First publication in Great Britain

PRINTING HISTORY
Bantam edition published 1996

This collection copyright © Capital Radio plc 1996
Compiled by Chris Tarrant, Mitch Symons and Susan Willer

Visit the 95.8 Capital FM website on www.CapitalFM.co.uk

Illustrations © John Taylor 1996

Bantam Books are published by Transworld Publishers Ltd,
61-63 Uxbridge Road, London W5 5SA,
in Australia by Transworld Publishers (Australia) Pty Ltd,
15-25 Helles Avenue, Moorebank, NSW 2170,
and in New Zealand by Transworld Publishers (NZ) Ltd,
3 William Pickering Drive, Albany, Auckland.

Reproduced, printed and bound in Great Britain by
Cox & Wyman Ltd, Reading, Berks.

Introduction

AFTER THE HUGE, AND TOTALLY UNEXPECTED AND thoroughly undeserved success of the *Dangly Bits* book, we've had thousands of people asking us if we're going to do a follow up... well hundreds of people... well at least dozens... well my mummy was quite keen! So, we decided to do the *Breakfast Show Book* to give us a chance to peep back at just a few of the ridiculous things we've been doing on the programme this year at some ungodly hour of the morning.

The **Dangly Bits** have always been hugely popular with our listeners and this year we introduced **Dangly Bits Part II**, which was, frankly, pretty much like **Dangly Bits Part I**, but it gave us a chance to set trivia questions about television, music, film, showbiz showbiz showbiz... and just about anything else we could find!

The **123 Game** ran for a couple of years and in that time we learnt some quite mind-bogglingly useless pieces of information. Not many would believe, for example, that Kim Basinger baths in lemon juice and sour cream, but she does! Or that John Cleese chose a papier mâché model of Margaret Thatcher and a baseball bat as his luxury items on Desert Island Discs, but he did! Or that Belinda Carlisle used to be a petrol pump attendant, but she was!

But the things that really get people talking, as usual, are all our wild, weird and wonderfully wacky stories from around the world. We must get through literally thousands every year and just when you think they can't possibly get any sillier, they do. So, we've included a selection of our favourite ones, like *'Swami Meditates At Bottom Of Lake For Six Days'*, *'Man Raids Bank Completely Naked'*, and *'Coconut Falls Off Holy Man's Head After It Has Been There For Fourteen Years'*!

We raised lots of money for our 'Help A London Child' charity with the first book, and we hope to do the same this year. Thank you for your contribution to a very worthy cause.

Best wishes from me and from all the Breakfast Show crew.

123 Game – Part I
Questions

1. Place these three rock stars in order of their age, listing the oldest first:

a)   Phil Collins
b)   Eric Clapton
c)   Elton John

2. Starting with the first, place these three people in the order in which they became President of the United States:

a)   Richard Nixon
b)   Lyndon Johnson
c)   Jimmy Carter

3. Starting with the planet closest to the sun, place these three planets in order of distance from the sun:

a) Earth
b) Mars
c) Mercury

4. Beginning with the lowest number, place these three bingo expressions in numerical order of the numbers they represent:

a) 'Unlucky for some'
b) 'Clickety-click'
c) 'Kelly's eye'

Hen-pecked hubby still hounded... from the grave!

Hector Murton's wife died in 1992, but he still hears from her regularly – in bizarre messages from beyond the grave.

Forty-nine-year-old Hector receives his wife's messages on the bottom of his television screen when he watches TV in the evening. The messages range from, 'Don't forget to pick up the dry cleaning' to 'How did Sylvia get on at her interview?' to 'Call your mother'!

'Betty never lets me forget anything,' says the jeweller from New York City. 'Her messages consist of ordinary chitchat, household advice, fashion tips... she even tells me when I'm running out of things and tells me to add toilet paper and toothpaste to my shopping list.'

'Sometimes it's just a few words from Betty,' says Hector fondly, 'but once it was a whole recipe for chicken cacciatore, just like she used to make it. But whatever it is, no matter how ordinary, I enjoy it. I know my Betty is with me day and night. And that's the most wonderful feeling in the world.'

Patient power!

A woman in Arizona was so fed up at having to wait two hours to see her doctor, that she billed him $50 an hour — and he agreed to pay it!

Harriet Runyon said the doctor didn't offer an explanation or apologize for making her wait, so when she got home she sent him a bill for $100. The stunned physician rang her up and demanded to know how she could possibly think her time was so valuable, but she pointed out that he had sent her a bill for $800 for a procedure that took twenty minutes.

The doctor backed down — and deducted $100 for her time!

Watermelon gets parking ticket!

Tough cops in Odense, Denmark, fined Lotte Merbus $30 for illegally parking a watermelon!

The housewife had apparently dropped it on a yellow line while loading her car with groceries!

5. Starting with the earliest, place these three Whitney Houston hits in the order in which they reached number one in the charts:

a) 'One Moment In Time'
b) 'I Will Always Love You'
c) 'I Wanna Dance With Somebody'

6. Place these three actresses in the order of their age, starting with the oldest first:

a) Demi Moore
b) Sharon Stone
c) Kim Basinger

7. Starting with the oldest, place these three chocolate bars in the order in which they were first put on sale in Britain:

a) Crunchie
b) Flake
c) Cadbury's Fruit and Nut

8. Place these three women in the order of the number of marriages they've had, beginning with the one with the most:

a) Joanna Lumley
b) Raquel Welch
c) Caron Keating

9. Beginning with the tallest, place these three stars in the order of their height:

a) Craig McLachlan
b) Elton John
c) David Bowie

10. Starting at the beginning of the calendar year, place these three star signs in the order of the months into which they fall:

a) Scorpio
b) Aquarius
c) Virgo

Fun Fact

①

Chris often jokes about Howard Hughes' undergarments and during the 'trade with Tarrant' competition he actually gave away Howard's string vest as a prize. Needless to say, it was a booby prize and the prizewinner was very disappointed. She had been trying to win £10,000 at the time!

95·8 **CAPITAL** FM

To love and to cherish for ever... and ever... and ever...

An astonishing one in five married couples were wed before in a previous life, according to a top reincarnation researcher.

'There is lots of new evidence that shows that the love relationship often runs from lifetime to lifetime,' says Bruce Goldberg, a leading hypnotherapist and past-life researcher. 'This can often explain the deep bonds of love and intimacy that some individuals feel instantly with another.'

Mr Goldberg found that when married couples underwent hypnotic regression, they frequently recalled being together in one or more past lives.

'It is quite an amazing discovery,' admits Mr Goldberg, 'and just goes to show... love never dies!'

11. Place these three important news events in the order in which they happened, starting with the earliest:

a)   The jailing for life of the Kray twins
b)   The assassination of President Kennedy
c)   The birth of the first test-tube baby

12. Starting with the earliest, place these three Demi Moore films in the order in which they were released in the UK:

a)   *A Few Good Men*
b)   *Disclosure*
c)   *Ghost*

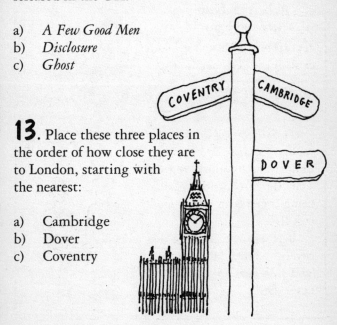

13. Place these three places in the order of how close they are to London, starting with the nearest:

a)   Cambridge
b)   Dover
c)   Coventry

14. Starting with the earliest, place these three artists in the order that they sang in the Eurovision Song Contest:

a) Michael Ball
b) Celine Dion
c) Sonia

15. Place these three actors in the order of their age, beginning with the youngest:

a) Robert de Niro
b) Harrison Ford
c) Jeremy Irons

Porkies
Questions

1. Here are three statements. Two of them are true, and one is a lie. Which one is the porkie?

a) **John Cleese** chose a life-sized papier-mâché model of Margaret Thatcher and a baseball bat as his luxuries on *Desert Island Discs*

b) **Cilla Black** chose 'Anyone Who Had A Heart' (by Cilla Black) as the record she would take on a desert island on *Desert Island Discs*

c) **Esther Rantzen** chose a guitar as her luxury on *Desert Island Discs*

Man must prove he didn't die!

James McGehee couldn't believe his ears when he rang the social security administration department to find out why his social security cheque had been stopped – and they told him it was because he was dead!

Government officials said their records showed him as 'deceased' and even froze his bank account so that he couldn't get any money out.

Sixty-year-old James, from Fort Worth, Texas, eventually turned up at the social security offices in person – to prove he was alive and well – but was told turning up alive was not proof enough that he hadn't died!

Stuntman shoves snake up his nose!

A local snake-swallower in Bombay, India shoves an eighteen-inch serpent up his nose so far that the reptile's body curves its head and comes crawling out of the man's mouth!

2. Which of the following is the porkie?

a) **Jo Brand** was a psychiatric nurse before she became a comedienne
b) **Jim Carrey**'s first job was as a clown at children's parties
c) **Axl Rose** used to earn $8.00 an hour for smoking cigarettes

3. Which of the following is the porkie?

a) **Phil Collins** collects model railways
b) **Kim Basinger** collects dictionaries
c) **Claudia Schiffer** collects crucifixes

4. Which of these statements is not true?

a) **George Michael** used to work in British Home Stores
b) **Madonna** used to work in McDonald's
c) **Brian Conley** used to work in Dixons

5. Which of the following is the porkie?

a) **Sting**'s father was a milkman named Ernie
b) **David Bowie**'s father owned a Soho wrestling club
c) **Mick Jagger**'s father was an undertaker

Sleepy teen leaps to safety

Sleepwalking teenager Hugo Schmauz crashed through the window of his hotel room, plunged twelve storeys to the ground below – and survived with barely a scratch!

And incredibly, eighteen-year-old Hugo was sleeping so soundly that the hair-raising fall didn't even wake him up!

'Nobody could survive a fall like that if they were awake,' said Dr Franz Rohm, 'but apparently this young man was so relaxed that his body was able to absorb the impact of his crash landing.'

Witnesses had to wake Hugo up after his fall, to tell him what had just happened!

Man pays off ex-wife — with the shirt off his back!

When Gary Mertz was told to pay his ex-wife $56,200 in their divorce settlement, he took the shirt off his back and gave that to her too!

The fifty-one-year-old toolmaker took his top off as soon as he heard the judge's decision, and wrote on the back, 'I pay Marilyn Mertz the sum of $56,200... and the shirt off my back too.' A bank clerk at the Harrison Township Bank in Michigan said the 'cheque' would be legal tender — but warned it would probably take an extra day to cash it!

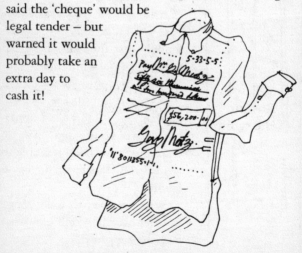

6. Which of these three statements is a lie?

a) **John Cleese**'s middle name is Marwood
b) **Jonathan Ross**'s middle name is Rupert
c) **Dustin Hoffman**'s middle name is Lee

7. Which of the following is not true?

a) **Jeremy Irons** was a policeman before he became an actor
b) **Jane Seymour** used to be a ballet dancer
c) **Paula Abdul** was Janet Jackson's choreographer before starting on her own singing career

8. Which of these is the porkie?

a) **Jonathan Ross** has a degree in East European Modern History
b) **Rowan Atkinson** has a degree in Law
c) **Harry Enfield** has a degree in Politics

9. Which of these three statements is the porkie?

a) **Pierce Brosnan** was offered the lead in *Raiders of the Lost Ark* before Harrison Ford
b) **John Travolta** was offered the lead in *An Officer and a Gentleman* before Richard Gere
c) **Frank Sinatra** was offered the lead in *Dirty Harry* before Clint Eastwood

10. Which of these is a lie?

a) In 1957 a woman named Esther Lawson left her sister £40,000 on the condition that she wore the same dress for a year!
b) In 1960 a man named Samuel Bratt, whose wife wouldn't let him smoke, left her £330,000 on the condition that she smoked five cigars a day for the rest of her life
c) In 1974 a dentist named Philip Grundy left his dental nurse £181,000 on the condition that she didn't go out with men or wear any make-up or jewellery for five years

Coin-happy clown arrested!

Authorities in Santa Cruz, California, are threatening to throw a happy-go-lucky professional clown in jail – for feeding coins into parking meters so that drivers won't get a ticket!

'I've been walking up and down the streets in my clown outfit feeding meters for six years,' says Mr Twister the Clown, 'because I like to make people happy. But now the cops are giving me a hard time, because they say I am costing the city an estimated $70,000 a year in parking fines!'

Mr Twister says he spends nearly $1,000 of his own money each year making sure tourists and shoppers aren't ticketed while they are away from their cars. 'I can go to sleep every night knowing I've helped someone,' says the twenty-six-year-old clown. 'If the police want to throw me in jail for that, then they can... I'm a clown and I'm just doing my job!'

Snake crawls 1,200 miles to find its owner!

When Randall Darby moved to Pennsylvania his pet snake had gone missing so he had to leave it behind, and never thought he would see it again – until the day the twelve-foot-long boa constrictor showed up at his front door!

'I've heard of dogs and cats following their owners across the country,' said Darby, 'but I would never have imagined that a snake could come all this way. It's almost 1,200 miles for heaven's sake!

'I guess animals have keen instincts that humans can't begin to understand,' said a delighted Darby. 'I'll be extra careful not to let him escape again – in case he heads back to Florida!'

Nose-picking gene discovered!

If you have a habit of picking your nose, it's not your fault – you were born with it.

Scientists in Sydney, Australia, have now isolated the gene that causes people to pick their noses!

11. Which of the following is the porkie?

a) **Anne Robinson** lists 'moving house' as one of her recreations in Debrett's *People of Today*

b) **Woody Allen** lists 'chocolate milkshakes' as one of his recreations in *International Who's Who*

c) **Anthea Turner** lists 'collecting watches' as her hobby in *Who's Who On The Television*

12. Which of these three statements is not true?

a) **Boy George** once appeared as a guest on *The A-Team*

b) **Shakin' Stevens** once appeared as a guest on *Happy Days*

c) **Sheena Easton** once appeared as a guest star on *Miami Vice*

13. Which of these is a lie?

a) **Clint Eastwood**'s film debut was playing a lab technician in *Revenge of the Creature*

b) **Mel Gibson**'s film debut was playing a surfer in *Summer City*

c) **Harrison Ford**'s film debut was playing a masochistic dental patient in *The Little Shop of Horrors*

14. Which of these three statements is the porkie?

a) Philosopher John Stuart Mill read Greek fluently at the age of three

b) Tennis player Tracy Austin appeared on the cover of *World Tennis Magazine* at the age of four

c) Violinist Yehudi Menuhin made his concert debut at the age of five

Frenchman's fishy phobia

An employee of an aquarium was given fourteen days off work with pay – because the fish made him nervous by constantly looking at him! A French court ordered security guard Michel Vichy's boss to pay for his leave, ruling that his disorder was work-related.

'The fish were looking at me all the time, every-where I went,' Vichy said. 'I just couldn't stand it!'

Dangly Bits – Part II

THE EAGERLY AWAITED SEQUEL

Questions

1. Which actress was a former backing singer for Marie Wilson and has appeared on TV in *The Manageress*, *Bergerac*, *The Word* and *Eastenders*?

2. What long-running TV soap did Onslow from *Keeping Up Appearances* star in, and what was his character's name?

3. Which actress made her TV debut in a Fairy Liquid commercial in 1964 – aged four – and is the sister of a former Hot Gossip dancer?

4. Which TV personality worked as a hairdresser, with clients including Shirley Bassey and Lulu, before entering showbiz, and was warm-up man for *Are You Being Served?*, *Little and Large* and *The Marti Caine Show*?

5. Who met her famous husband at a beauty competition and then became a hostess on his TV game show?

6. Can you name the prison featured in *Porridge*, and what was the sequel called?

7. Who am I?

- This actor, TV presenter and writer was born on 6 January in Banstead, Surrey
- He graduated from Oxford University
- In 1991 he won the British Comedy Award's 'Best TV Newcomer', and in 1992 he won the British Press Guild 'Best Comedy Performer' Award
- He has presented the 'Bore of the Year Awards'

and in 1995 he presented one of the awards at the Comedy Awards

- He co-wrote *OTT* and introduced the word 'bonking' into the English language
- He has appeared on many TV shows including *Mr Bean*, *Bad Company* and *In Search of Happiness*
- He has hosted the last five series of *Have I Got News For You*

8. Who am I?

- This actress was born in York on 9 December 1934 and went to The Mount School in York
- Her star sign is Sagittarius
- She wanted to be a designer and attended art school for a year before training at the Central School of Speech and Drama
- Her hobbies include painting, drawing, sewing and tapestry
- She won the BAFTA for Best Actress of the Year in 1981 and was voted 'Funniest Female' on TV in 1982 by *TV Times* readers
- Her autobiography is called *A Great Deal of Laughter*
- She made her professional acting debut as Ophelia in *Hamlet* in 1957 with the Old Vic in Liverpool
- She received an OBE in 1988

- Her TV appearances include *Z-Cars*, *The Morecambe and Wise Show*, *The Cherry Orchard*, *As Time Goes By* and *A Fine Romance*
- She is married to actor Michael Williams and has one daughter

9. Who am I?

- This actress was born in Hull on 10 May 1946
- She was educated at Newland High School in Hull and studied drama at LAMDA
- She is married to playwright Jack Rosenthal and has one daughter and one son
- She writes a monthly column for *Good Housekeeping* and has written many books, her latest one entitled *You Can Read Me Like A Book*
- She has a cat called Pushkin
- In *Who's Who* she lists her hobby as 'finding time to think of one!'
- Her TV appearances include *Doctor at Large*, *The Sweeney*, *Give Us A Clue*, *Blankety Blank*, *Have I Got News For You* and *Room 101*
- She once won the *TV Times* 'Best Comedy Actress' award for *All At Number Twenty*
- She stars in the TV comedy series *Agony* and was Beattie in the British Telecom ads

Fun Fact

②

The Breakfast Show's April Fool's Day jokes have become legendary, and this year the joke focused around a brand-new weathergirl called Suzie Snapple. Chris Tarrant had been away for two weeks so listeners were led to believe that Suzie had been recruited in his absence. Suzie had the most irritating voice ever heard on air and the phone lines quickly jammed up with listeners begging for Suzie to be taken off immediately. Strangely enough, there were a couple of callers who thought she was very good!

95·8 CAPITAL FM

Mind power suspends toilet paper!

Scientists at the Sergei Virshov University in Moscow have confirmed that psychic Yuri Tashrinko is able to suspend up to fifteen rolls of toilet paper in the air — using only the power of his mind!

The fifty-nine-year-old fish merchant, whose amazing powers have been authenticated under laboratory conditions, can't explain why he's only able to perform the mind-over-matter feat with bathroom tissue, and nothing else!

Two year old breaks into bank vault!

Stunned bank officials urgently revised their security precautions after a two-year-old toddler wandered away from his mother — and accidentally opened the bank vault!

Dumped girl dumps rocks onto boyfriend's car!

Hotheaded secretary Elke Timmerman got so angry when her fiancé suggested they postpone their wedding that she stormed out of his house – and covered his car with half a ton of rocks!

'I was absolutely stunned when I came out of the house the next morning to go to work,' said twenty-nine-year-old Harold Kniss. 'I simply couldn't figure out how she did it. She's only small and it must have taken her all night to round up all those rocks and hoist them onto my car. She must have been exhausted.

'She was obviously very angry with me but I'm determined to make things up with her. Any lady who'd move half a ton of rocks just for me is the kind of lady I want to marry!'

10. Who am I?

- This actress was born in India in 1946, and grew up in Malaysia
- She tried modelling before acting
- She played Ken Barlow's girlfriend in *Coronation Street* for eight weeks in the 1960s
- She's been a Bond girl
- She started a hair craze in 1976
- She's been bitten by Dracula and played opposite Steed in the late 1970s

11. In *The Magic Roundabout*, what were the names of:

a) the flower-chewing pink spotted cow?
b) the ill-tempered, egoist dog?
c) the resigned but cheerful snail?
d) the laid-back, spaced-out, hippy rabbit?
e) the jack-in-the-box?

12. Which *Coronation Street* actress, born Shirley Ann Broadbent, trained in ballet before becoming a chorus girl in London at the age of fourteen, and has danced on stage with Lionel Blair and Danny La Rue?

Latest French cuisine!

The hottest new item for tourists in France is a postcard to send home to your friends... for them to eat!

The cards come in six flavours and are ready to eat after thirty seconds in a microwave.

Pilgrims' progress... in the nude!

Police in Chandragutti, India, have been working feverishly to stop thousands of religious pilgrims from visiting a hilltop temple – stark naked!

Once a year, for many centuries, as many as three thousand devout Hindus – both male and female – have journeyed to this remote village for a week-long festival celebrating the goddess Renukamba, stripped to their birthday suits. But the bizarre practice has now been outlawed and armed police have already descended on the small village to make sure worshippers keep all their clothes on this year.

13. Which film is this line from: 'It is impossible for a man and a woman to have a successful relationship without sex getting in the way'?

14. Which actress has appeared in *Coronation Street*, *Emmerdale* and *Brookside*?

15. What connects Mary Poppins and Frank Spencer?

16. What was the name of the drinking establishment that Arthur Daley frequented in *Minder*, and what was the barman's name?

17. Which current *Eastenders* star has had a number one hit?

18. Which pop star has only eaten one meal a day since 1961, when he was described as 'chubby' on *Coronation Street*?

Fun Fact

3

95.8 Capital FM listeners often prove to be big-hearted people. When a contestant called George gambled — and lost — all the money he'd won on the Breakfast Show, winning only a paperclip, it seemed like the whole of London felt sorry for him. As it was St Valentine's Day, a limo firm rang and offered him and his wife a chauffeur for the night, and a top London restaurant treated him to VIP service for the evening. George had the time of his life and, to top it all, the next morning the sponsors, 'Lukcy Lotto', offered him £1,000 for the paperclip because they wanted to hang it on their wall!

95·8 CAPITAL FM

Sad farewell to a king

Nearly one thousand mourners attended a $91,000 funeral in New Delhi, India for thirty-eight-year-old Bobaba... a fifteen-foot king cobra!

The popular snake had been the mascot of the famed Mehta Institute, which has taught three generations of snake charmers since its founding in 1920. Bobaba died of natural causes and his lavish funeral was paid for by more than six hundred former Mehta students, their families and friends.

Bobaba is remembered as an intelligent, friendly creature who helped train some of India's best mystics in the snake charmer's art.

Cheating wives and hubbies glow in the dark!

A judge in Dacca, Bangladesh, is ordering married men and women found guilty of infidelity to have their teeth painted with permanent glow-in-the-dark paint — so that others are aware of their low morals.

The bizarre punishment, which has affected forty-eight men and twelve women so far, has been challenged in an appeals court!

19. Who is comedian Jim Moir better known as?

20. What film is this line from, and who said it? 'Is everybody in, is everybody in, the ceremony is about to begin.'

21. The drawing of which Walt Disney character was based on Marilyn Monroe?

22. Which artist has appeared on the British album charts for at least one week in every year of the chart's thirty-seven years of existence?

23. Which film legend started his working life as a handyman and unblocked Tennessee Williams's loo and mended his fuses before auditioning for one of his plays?

24. What is the link between *Soldier, Soldier* and *Auf Wiedersehen Pet*?

25. Which Emmy Award-winning actress wrote her autobiography in 1989 and called it *Stare Back And Smile*?

26. Which actor, born in November 1949, was the son of an attorney-general and trained at Arts Educational School? He left acting for a while to work in the wine trade and then became a researcher on Jimmy Young's BBC Radio 2 show. His TV appearances include *Richard II*, *Upstairs, Downstairs* and *Winston Churchill – The Wilderness Years*.

27. What is the connection between Clive James and Adrian Edmondson?

28. Which TV presenter wrote the book *How To Be Utterly Brilliant*?

29. Which actor has appeared in all of these TV shows: *Z-Cars*, *The Sweeney*, *Minder*, *Bergerac*, *Coronation Street*, *Auf Wiedersehen Pet*, *Dempsey and Makepeace*, *Shine On Harvey Moon* and *The Bill*?

Jungle tribe... from Mars!

Scientists have come across an African jungle tribe that they say came from Mars – in 1820!

'This is the scientific find of the century,' Dr Signe Winslof told reporters in Boras, Sweden. 'The extraterrestrials have totally acclimated themselves to a primitive jungle existence in Africa.

'The Martian tribesmen are black and look just like humans with the exception of their eyes, which are completely white,' says Dr Winslof. 'They show a fondness for hoops and circles and seem to be able to speak every single language known to man.

'Why the extraterrestrials choose to live as savages in the jungle isn't clear,' adds Dr Winslof, 'but it might be some kind of revolt – against the highly technical, impersonal lives they and their ancestors led on Mars.'

The tale of the patient bank bandit

A bungling bank robber was arrested by police in Fort Worth, Texas, after he put on a ski mask... and then patiently stood at the back of the queue!

An alert customer noticed the disguise and hurried to the police station – which was right next door. The surprised crook was nabbed by cops when he was just two from the front of the queue.

Caught napping

Many office workers take tiny naps every day while watching a computer screen – and don't even know it!

The naps – called 'micro-sleeps' – come on suddenly and last for only a few seconds, says Asa Kilbom, a Swedish Occupational Health Specialist.

30. Name the seven dwarfs.

31. Who once made her chauffeur do a U-turn in her Rolls, after screaming at him, 'Alderson, you fool – you've let me come without my eyelashes!'?

32. Which actress sang in two bands and then formed her own record label (called Visual Records) in 1986, before appearing on TV in *Alas Smith and Jones*, *Hale and Pace*, *Watch With Mother* and *The Bill*, and now stars in the same soap as her husband?

Swami's sensational six-day meditation

A seventy-year-old guru meditated on the bottom of a lake for six full days, then swam to the shore completely unharmed!

Followers who stood vigil by the shores of the sixty-foot-deep lake in Rewa, India, claimed it was a miracle, but the grey-haired guru, Ravindra Mishra, refused to take credit for the amazing feat and said, 'The Hindu goddess Kali helped me go without air for 144 hours – all glory is hers!'

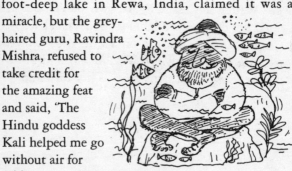

The biggest goof in Hollywood history

The biggest goof in Hollywood history was the title of the 1968 movie *Krakatoa, East of Java*... that's because the island of Krakatoa is two hundred miles west of Java!

123 Game — Part II
Questions

1. Only one of the following statements about the two actresses, **Elizabeth Taylor** and **Marilyn Monroe**, is true. Which one is it?

a)   Both converted to Judaism
b)   Both had an obsession with the number eight
c)   Both married before the age of sixteen

2. One of these three facts is true about both of these people, the other two are rubbish. The two people are **Engelbert Humperdinck** and **Bjorn Borg**. Which one of these statements is true about them both?

a)   Both own horses which have won at Royal Ascot
b)   Both are chocoholics
c)   Both have launched fragrances

3. Only one of the following statements is true of both **Carly Simon** and **Whoopi Goldberg**. Which is it?

a)   Both have private pilots' licences
b)   Both have lived with Jack Nicholson
c)   Both have written children's books

4. Only one of these three facts is true about both **Charlie Chaplin** and **Eva Peron**. Which is it?

a)   Both married seven times
b)   Both were buried twice
c)   Both were colour blind

5. Which one of the following statements about the two supermodels, **Jerry Hall** and **Marie Helvin**, is true?

a)   Both used to work as librarians
b)   Both have performed in ballets
c)   Both hate their feet

Dog fetches 149 newspapers!

Dog owner Dick Stephens told his pet Rottweiler to 'fetch' the morning paper, but the excited dog got a bit carried away and came back with 149 of them!

The confused pet scoured the neighbourhood grabbing every newspaper he could clamp his teeth on, and when stunned Stephens opened his front door at 7 a.m. he found piles of soggy rolled up morning papers on the front porch.

Stephens and his wife Anne returned as many of the papers as possible, but had to call round local newsagents to try and find out where they all came from. 'It was very embarrassing,' said Stephens, 'and our dog couldn't believe his eyes when we started taking back all the papers he'd just spent an hour rounding up. I'll definitely be getting the paper myself in future!'

One man in a tub with five-foot python!

A forty-two-year-old man got the shock of his life when he slipped into a warm tub to soak, and came face to face with a deadly five-foot python!

Loki Singh, from New Delhi, India, returned home from work on Friday night when his wife ran him a warm bubble bath to soak in.

'I was relaxing in the tub when suddenly I felt something move past my leg and curl around my ankle,' the young dad told reporters with a shudder. 'Since we have four young children, I assumed a toy had fallen in, so I grabbed it and pulled it out of the water... and found myself looking straight into the eyes of a deadly python!'

Singh says that luckily he had grabbed the snake around its neck, and managed to get out of the bath without it being able to bite him.

Neither Singh nor his wife know how the snake got into the bath... but he says he will definitely be showering in future!

6. Only one of these statements is true of both **Sir Cliff Richard** and **Terry Venables**. Which is it?

a)   Both are members of the Dennis the Menace Fan Club
b)   Both were born with two livers
c)   Both have been awarded the Freedom of the City of London

7. Only one of these facts is true of both **Bryan Ferry** and **Paul Young**. Which one is it?

a)   Both have survived light aeroplane crashes
b)   Both used to be hairdressers
c)   Both named their children after Motown stars

8. Which one of these three statements is true of both **Richard Wilson** and **Gloria Hunniford**?

a)   Both have made their own fitness videos
b)   Both have written cookery books
c)   Both have appeared in advertisements for Coca-Cola

9. Which one of these three statements is true of both **Kim Basinger** and **Demi Moore**?

a)   Both have had hypnosis to cure them of a phobia
b)   Both have never learnt to drive a car
c)   Both have bought their own town in America

10. Only one of the following facts is true of both **Clint Eastwood** and **William Shatner**. Which is it?

a)   Both actively took part in a campaign in America to try and get gun laws tightened
b)   Both put up $50,000 for a group of mercenaries to rescue American prisoners left in Cambodia after the Vietnam war
c)   Both have run for Congress – but were not elected

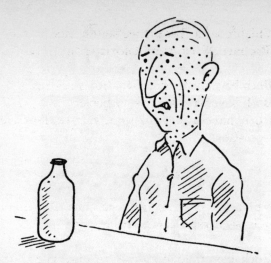

11. Which one of these three facts is true of both
Sir David Attenborough and **Noel Gallagher**?

a)   Both can't drive a car
b)   Both are allergic to dairy products
c)   Both never wear a watch

Fun Fact

4

The Breakfast Show world tour has been broadcast live from Kenya, Australia, Tasmania, Los Angeles, New York, Gibraltar, Lapland, Hawaii, the River Thames and Billingsgate Fish Market!

95·8 CAPITAL FM

123 Game — Part I
Answers

1.
  b)   Eric Clapton (March 1945)
  c)   Elton John (March 1947)
  a)   Phil Collins (January 1951)

2.
  b)   Lyndon Johnson (1963-1969)
  a)   Richard Nixon (1969-1974)
  c)   Jimmy Carter (1977-1981)

3.
  c)   Mercury (5.8 million km from the sun)
  a)   Earth (150 million km)
  b)   Mars (228 million km)

4.
   c)   'Kelly's eye' is number one
   a)   'Unlucky for some' is number 13
   b)   'Clickety-click' is number 66

5.
   c)   'I Wanna Dance With Somebody' – May 1987
   a)   'One Moment In Time' – September 1988
   b)   'I Will Always Love You' – November 1992

6.
   c)   Kim Basinger was born on 8 December 1953
   b)   Sharon Stone was born on 10 March 1958
   a)   Demi Moore was born on 11 November 1962

7.
   b)   Flake is the oldest – it was launched in 1911
   c)   Fruit and Nut followed in 1921
   a)   Crunchie was introduced in 1929

New pocket-sized space alien detector

Dutch inventor Dak Gjerstad hopes to make millions with his latest brainchild – a pocket-sized device that will detect space aliens.

Gjerstad says the gadget is small enough to carry in a shirt pocket and emits a steady vibration when a space alien gets too close for comfort!

Man robs bank... completely naked!

Police in Vienna, Austria, are searching for a cheeky chap who held up a suburban bank... completely naked.

'His disguise was absolutely perfect,' said a police spokesman. 'The bank was full of female staff and customers but not one of them could describe the guy's face!'

8.
b) Raquel Welch has had three husbands – James Welch, Patrick Curtis and Andre Weinfeld.

a) Joanna Lumley has married twice – to Jeremy Lloyd and Stephen Barlow

c) Caron Keating has had one husband – Russ Lindsey

9.
a) Craig McLachlan is the tallest at six foot
c) David Bowie is next at 5'10"
b) Elton John is the smallest at 5'8"

10.
b) Aquarius is January 20 – February 19
c) Virgo is August 24 – September 23
a) Scorpio is October 24 – November 22

11.
b) The assassination of President Kennedy was in 1963

a) The jailing for life of the Kray twins was in 1969

c) The birth of the first test-tube baby was in 1978

12. c) *Ghost* (with Patrick Swayze) was released in 1990

    a) *A Few Good Men* (with Tom Cruise and Jack Nicholson) was released in 1993

    b) *Disclosure* (with Michael Douglas) was released in 1995

13. a) Cambridge is the nearest – it is 53 miles from London

    b) Dover is next – it is 71 miles away

    c) Coventry is the furthest – it is 86 miles from London

14. b) Celine Dion represented Switzerland in the Eurovision Song Contest in 1988 – and won (with 'Ne Partez Sans Moi')

    a) Michael Ball represented the UK in 1992 – and came second (with 'One Step Out Of Time')

    c) Sonia represented the UK in 1993 – and came second (with 'Better The Devil You Know')

15.
c) Jeremy Irons was born in 1948
a) Robert de Niro was born in 1943
b) Harrison Ford was born in 1942

Cow manure found in award-winning chilli!

Super chef Geraldo Renaldez won more than two hundred awards for his delicious chilli – before his ex-wife revealed his secret ingredients are... cow manure and milk of magnesia!

The acclaimed Mexican cook lost his high-paying job at an Acapulco restaurant when his secret got out, but the forty-three-year-old father of five insists his chilli is completely harmless!

'Fresh cow manure adds a rich dark quality to the chilli,' says Renaldez, 'and the milk of magnesia smoothes it and gives it a lovely texture. Without these ingredients my chilli would not be the greatest chilli the world has ever tasted.

'People are outraged now,' says Renaldez, 'but they will soon realize that they've been eating my chilli for years without ever getting sick. It's delicious and, once people have got over the initial shock, they'll be clamouring for it again... and then everyone will want to hire me!'

Porkies
Answers

1. c) is the porkie. Esther Rantzen actually chose bath salts.

2. b) is the porkie. Jim Carrey was in fact a toilet cleaner. (Jo Brand says it was her job as a psychiatric nurse that helped her discover she had a talent for making people laugh, and Axl Rose was hired to smoke cigarettes by UCLA for a science experiment.)

3. c) is the porkie. (Phil Collins does collect model railways, although he was once forced to sell his Hornby Double-O train set because he needed the money, and Kim Basinger collects dictionaries. She says it all started when her screen star hubby Alec Baldwin bought her her first one.)

4. c) is not true. (George Michael had a Saturday job in BHS in Wembley when he was at school, and Madonna used to work in both McDonald's and Burger King!)

5. c) is the porkie.

6. b) is a complete lie. Jonathan Ross's middle name is actually Stephen.

Holy man hooked up!

Hindu mystic Ravi Varanasi has been hanging three feet in the air by eight steel hooks embedded in his flesh for a world record eighty-seven days – and he says he's never felt better!

'I feel no pain or discomfort,' says the amazing holy man. 'I have learned to direct my attention away from the physical body, and prove that what is important in life is the mind – not the body.'

Varanasi has eight steel hooks embedded into the flesh of his back and legs, as well as several stick pins in his arms and an eight-inch needle through his tongue.

His followers watch over him constantly, giving him food and water when he needs it, but doctors report that he is in good condition and Varanasi says that he is enjoying the demonstration so much he may well stay up there for a whole year!

Seven-month Spanish course?

A woman stunned doctors when she woke up from a seven-month coma speaking fluent Spanish... although she'd never heard a word of the language before.

Li Hau-Jung's amazing case is being closely studied by reincarnation experts.

7. a) is not true. Jeremy Irons was actually a Social Worker. (Jane Seymour was a ballet dancer and danced with the London Festival Ballet at the age of thirteen, and Paula Abdul was, indeed, Janet Jackson's choreographer.)

8. b) is the porkie. Rowan Atkinson's degree is in Electrical Engineering.

9. a) is the porkie. Pierce Brosnan wasn't offered the lead in *Raiders of the Lost Ark*... but Tom Selleck was.

10. a) is a lie. The other two are both true.

11. c) is the porkie. Anthea Turner doesn't list collecting watches as her hobby, but actress Amanda Burton does.

12. b) is the porkie. Shakin' Stevens never appeared on *Happy Days*... but both Tom Hanks and Suzi Quatro did!

13. c) is a lie. The part of the masochistic dental patient was actually played by a young Jack Nicholson. Harrison Ford's film debut was playing a bellboy in *Dead Heat On A Merry-Go-Round*.

14. c) is the porkie, of course! Yehudi Menuhin made his concert debut at the age of seven.

Toddler's valuable flush!

Two-year-old Paul Deseau spotted his mum's diamond engagement and wedding rings, and a diamond and ruby ring on the bathroom sink – and flushed the lot down the loo!

'I'd put them there while I cleaned the bathroom,' said the toddler's heartbroken mother. 'I suddenly heard the flush on the toilet go and when I turned round I realized what my son had done. I couldn't believe my eyes.

'It's my fault for leaving them where Paul could reach them,' admitted the twenty-eight-year-old housewife. 'I know I'll never see them again, but some lucky person is going to find $12,500 worth of my jewellery!'

Loyal dog digs up ditched slippers!

A loyal dog showed he was the world's most faithful pet – when he travelled a mind-boggling eight miles to fetch his owner's slippers!

'I got Augie the bloodhound two years ago,' says Terry Pearson from Jackson, Mississippi, 'and immediately trained him to bring me my slippers the minute I got home from work, which he has done every day ever since.

'But then at Christmas I got a new pair of slippers,' says Terry, 'so I threw my old ones in the bin... but when I got home that night, instead of bringing me my new ones, Augie dug through the trash in the backyard and brought me the pair I'd thrown away!' So, to get rid of the slippers once and for all, Terry says he drove to a dump outside town – four miles away from his house – and threw them out. 'Augie was in the truck when I threw them in the dump,' says Terry, 'but I really didn't think he was taking much notice.'

However, when Terry got home from work the next day Augie had gone, and when he hadn't returned by 8 p.m. Terry went out looking for him. 'Just as I got to the end of the street I saw Augie walking towards me... with my old slippers in his mouth! I couldn't believe my eyes – he must have walked eight miles to get them, and crossed at least three main intersections on the way.

'He has obviously become very attached to the slippers and I really have no choice but to carry on wearing them,' says Terry. 'It's the least I can do really!'

Dangly Bits – Part II

THE EAGERLY AWAITED SEQUEL

Answers

1. Michelle Collins (Cindy from *Eastenders*)

2. Eddie Yates in *Coronation Street*

3. Leslie Ash (her sister is Debbie Ash)

4. Michael Barrymore

5. Anthea Redfern (she married Bruce Forsyth and was a hostess on *The Generation Game*)

6. The prison was Slade Prison, and the sequel was called *Going Straight*.

7. Angus Deayton

8. Dame Judi Dench

9. Maureen Lipman

10. Joanna Lumley

11.
   a) Ermintrude
   b) Dougal
   c) Brian
   d) Dylan
   e) Zebedee

12. Amanda Barrie (alias Alma, married to Mike Baldwin)

13. Billy Crystal said it in *When Harry Met Sally*.

14. Anna Friel. She played Belinda Johnson in *Coronation Street* when she was fourteen, Poppy Jarrat in *Emmerdale* when she was fifteen, and Beth Jordache in *Brookside* until recently.

15. The Dotrice family. Karen Dotrice starred in the film *Mary Poppins* and her sister Michele Dotrice was Frank Spencer's long-suffering wife, Betty, in the television comedy, *Some Mothers Do 'Ave 'Em*.

16. The Winchester Club. The barman's name was Dave.

17. Wendy Richard (Pauline Fowler) was top of the charts in 1962. She recorded 'Come Outside' with Mike Sarne and it shot to number one!

18. Cliff Richard

Lost and found...in the Atlantic Ocean!

When Larry Horner's wallet fell overboard during a deep-sea fishing trip, he accepted that he'd never see it again – but he was wrong... another fisherman hooked it six days later – and mailed it back to him!

'I couldn't believe my eyes when I opened my post,' said Larry. 'There was my lost wallet, complete with the $56, my driver's licence, and all my credit cards. I don't know what the chances are against that wallet ever being hooked in open waters off the Atlantic Ocean – but they have to be astronomical. I thought I had better odds of winning the national lottery than I did of ever seeing that wallet again. I'm very grateful to have it back!'

19. Vic Reeves

20. Val Kilmer as Jim Morrison in *The Doors*

21. Tinkerbell in *Peter Pan*

22. Elvis Presley

23. Marlon Brando

24. Tim Healy (Dennis in *Auf Wiedersehen Pet*) is married to Denise Welch (Marsha in *Soldier, Soldier*).

25. Joanna Lumley

26. Nigel Havers

27. 'Vivien' – Adrian Edmondson played the role of Vyvyan in *The Young Ones* and Clive James was born Vivien Clive James but never uses his first name.

28. Timmy Mallett

29. Kevin Lloyd (currently Detective Constable 'Tosh' Lines in *The Bill*)

30. Dopey, Sleepy, Happy, Grumpy, Sneezy, Doc and Bashful

31. Barbara Cartland

32. Claire King (Kim Tate in *Emmerdale*). She is married to Peter Amory (Chris Tate in *Emmerdale*).

Fourteen-year coconut feat!

A holy man in Calcutta, India, who balanced a coconut on his head for a mind-boggling fourteen years, stunned and devastated his devoted followers – when he tripped up, and the coconut fell to the ground and smashed open!

Guru Dilip Rao was worshipped by thousands who believed he was blessed with divine powers that had allowed him to keep the dried-up coconut carefully poised on his head since 1981.

But all the love and devotion Rao had earned went down the tubes when the prize coconut fell off, right in the middle of a worship festival in his honour. Reports say that many people broke down and cried, and Rao stormed off after the incident and went into seclusion!

Lemon juice fails to foil police!

Macarthur Wheeler, forty-six, of Pittsburgh, Pennsylvania was sentenced to twenty-four years in prison for bank robbery, after he and his accomplice were clearly seen on the bank's surveillance cameras – despite the fact that they'd rubbed their faces with lemon juice which they thought would blur their on-camera images!

Fun Fact

(5)

We've had some young people on the Breakfast Show but when Andrew Williams rang in one morning from the delivery suite of Queen Charlotte's Hospital to say that his wife was in labour, he put the telephone up to the monitor and the whole of London stopped and listened to the baby's heartbeat! Baby Oliver was born a few hours later — completely unaware that he was already famous!

95·8 CAPITAL FM

123 Game — Part II
Answers

1. a) is true of them both. Elizabeth Taylor converted to Judaism after marrying Mike Todd and Marilyn Monroe converted after marrying Arthur Miller.

2. c) is true of them both. Engelbert Humperdinck launched an aftershave called 'Release Me' and Bjorn Borg's fragrance was called 'Signature'.

3. c) is true of them both. Carly Simon wrote *Amy the Dancing Bear* and Whoopi Goldberg wrote *Alice*.

Robots to replace husbands by the year 2010!

A team of female scientists in Boston have created the perfect husband – a robot known as Kluden Z-443!

The android looks, sounds and feels almost exactly like a real man, and experts predict that by the year 2010, 64% of women will have one as a 'life partner' instead of a human husband.

'The Z-443 has all the advantages of a real man,' says Dr Nola Kluden, who designed the incredible robots, 'with none of the messy disadvantages.

'They're affectionate, patient and attentive. Their bodies are composed of a soft, flesh-like rubber and they are gentle, sensitive lovers. And the great thing is,' adds Dr Kluden, 'they won't leave their clothes all over the floor and they won't want to watch football or go to the pub every night.'

When the Z-443s go on the market, in the year 2000, women will be able to choose one of sixteen personality types including 'the rugged outdoors type', 'the strong silent type', 'the sensitive poet' and 'the worldly intellectual'.

'The human husband will soon be obsolete,' says Dr Kluden, who is already getting orders for the robots flooding in. 'The Z-443 will be everything any woman could wish for!'

4. b) is true of them both. Charlie Chaplin was buried in Switzerland when he died, but his body was stolen a few years later. When it was eventually recovered, he was buried again – this time in a vault surrounded by cement. Eva Peron's body was embalmed in Italy when she died, then moved to Madrid by her ex-husband and finally re-buried in Argentina.

5. c) is true of them both. A magazine survey asked various celebrities what they hated about their bodies and both Jerry Hall and Marie Helvin said they hated their feet. There was only one person asked who said they were perfectly happy with their body and wouldn't change anything, and that was Barbara Cartland. Chris Tarrant was in the survey too, and he said he hated his ears.

6. c) is true of them both. Basically this means they can drive their sheep over London Bridge and are exempt from paying market tolls!

7. c) is true of them both. Bryan Ferry called his son Otis, after Otis Redding, and Paul Young named his daughter Levi, after Levi Stubbs.

8. a) is true of them both. Richard Wilson made a fitness video called *Let's Dance* and Gloria Hunniford made one called *Fit For Life*.

9. c) is true of them both. Demi Moore and hubby Bruce Willis bought the town of Hailey (a ski resort in Idaho) after falling in love with it when they drove through it once. They bought it because they didn't want it ever to change! And Kim Basinger bought the town of Braselton in Georgia — but later had to sell it when she hit financial problems.

10. b) is true of them both — but the rescue wasn't successful.

11. a) is true of them both. Sir David made a conscious decision never to drive — and has lived seventy years without getting behind the wheel. Noel Gallagher can't drive either — in fact he says, 'I can't even walk straight, let alone drive a car!'

Fun Fact

6

The Breakfast Show has been broadcast from some very strange places over the years but the strangest of all came from the Masai Mara reserve in Kenya. Chris broadcast the show each morning surrounded by Masai warriors who jumped up and down with spears, while lions ate their breakfast and baboons raided his bag — all just yards from where he was sitting!

95·8 CAPITAL FM

Mouth-to-beak resuscitation revives frozen chicken!

Farmer Janet Bonney found a hen frozen solid under her front porch — and revived her with heat treatments and mouth-to-beak resuscitation! The miracle bird is up and running again, and has even laid an egg.

'She was lying there legs up, frozen solid,' recalls Mrs Bonney. 'I wanted to put her in a shoebox to bury her but her legs wouldn't bend so I rested her on a hot water bottle to thaw out. A few minutes later I felt the bird's heartbeat so I gave her some quick mouth-to-beak resuscitation — and incredibly the chicken got to her feet and clucked. It was a wonderful moment!'